CHARLIE

by James Driscoll
Illustrated by Rob Lee

Storm Publishing

Charlie has been a clown in the circus for most of his life.

The Shoe People think that Charlie is the funniest clown in the whole world. There is never a dull moment in Shoe Town when he is around because he makes everybody laugh so much with some of the funny things he does.

Charlie lives at the end of Shoe Street next door to Trampy. He lives in a very special house.

Charlie's house is exactly the same shape as a circus tent and very brightly coloured. A circus tent is called a Big Top so Charlie calls his house The Little Big Top.

The Little Big Top has a garden which looks very odd at first sight. It is full of washing lines.

There are four washing lines attached to eight wooden posts. Some of the lines cross over one another making criss-cross patterns. Leaning against one of the wooden posts is a step-ladder.

Can you guess the reason for such a strange looking garden?

Charlie loves to walk the tight rope and he spends hours and hours practising on the washing lines in his garden.

He walks along one of the lines to the middle, bounces up and down, and jumps to another line as he lands. His favourite trick is to bounce high into the air, turn two backward somersaults and then land back perfectly on the tight rope.

The Shoe People love to watch Charlie performing his clever tricks.

The inside of The Little Big Top looks just like a circus ring.

There is not a carpet to be seen on the floor, instead Charlie has spread sawdust all over the ring.

At the start of each day one of Charlie's first jobs is to take a big rake and rake over the sawdust, smoothing it out so that it looks like a carpet. When you visit Charlie, the smell of the sawdust makes you think that you really are at the circus.

In the middle of the ring, there is a big round table with five bright red stars painted on top of it. The table was once used as a stand by the big elephants when they did their tricks.

There are also four smaller stands with yellow stars which Charlie uses as stools.

A trapeze hangs from the roof of The Little Big Top.

There is also a rope attached to the roof which dangles to the floor close to the trapeze. Charlie pulls himself up the rope to the trapeze and starts to swing backwards and forwards.

There is one very special trick that he is always asked to perform.

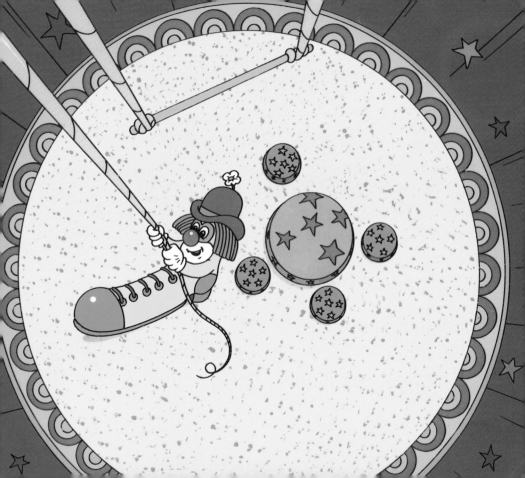

Charlie makes the trapeze swing faster and faster taking him high into the roof of the tent. When he is almost touching the canvas in the roof he lets go of the trapeze, turns twice in mid-air and catches the trapeze by his fingertips as it swings back.

The sight of Charlie performing his trick makes everyone gasp.

Charlie lives next door to Trampy and often when he is tightrope walking he looks over the fence to talk to Trampy. They are great friends.

Charlie says, "Hello Trampy, how are you today?" Trampy answers, "I'm fine thank you Charlie, and how are you?"

When Charlie is practising his tightrope act his answer is always the same. "Very well, thank you Trampy. I'm having a BOUNCIFUL time!" he replies as he bounces up and down on his washing line tightrope.

When the Shoe People are feeling miserable, there is always one person who can be relied on to cheer them up and make them laugh — Charlie.

He pulls silly faces and makes his hair stand on end. Often he squirts water from the daisy on the top of his hat.

They all think he is absolutely marvellous.

There are times when Charlie thinks back to his days in the circus when he performed in front of large crowds in The Big Top.

He has many fond memories of those days but never wishes to return to The Big Top.

He is very happy to be Charlie the clown who lives in the magic world of . . .

. . . The Shoe People.